Playing
with f

This book belongs to

_____

Written by Stephen Barnett
Illustrated by Rosie Brooks

Contents

Playing with friends 3

New words 31

What did you learn? 32

About this book

This story uses childhood play with friends as a bridge between what the reader is familiar with and new additions to his or her vocabulary.

Playing with friends

Paul

Jan

Paul, Jan and me

We all are friends.

We play together.

The ball

The ball is blue.

We are playing with the ball.

The cat is sleeping.

Paul
has the ball.

Jan
has the ball.

The cat wakes up.

The cat chases the ball.

We chase
the cat.

New words

friend

play

sleep

up

What did you learn?

What are the names of the friends?

What is the colour of the ball?

What is the colour of the cat?